By

Julian Hanshaw.

the Art OF
PHỞ

Julian Hanshaw

Jonathan Cafe
London

Published by Jonathan Cape.

2 4 6 8 1 0 9 7 5 3 1

Copyright © Julian Hanshaw 2010

First published in Great Britain in 2010 by Jonathan Cape Random House, 20 Vauxhall Bridge Road London. SW1V 2SA.

www.rbooks.co.uk

Addresses for Random House Can be found www.randomhou

Companies within the Group limited at se.co.uk/offices.htm

THE RANDOM House Group Limited reg no. 954009

A CIP catalogue record for this book is available from the British Library

Printed and bound in China by C and C offset printing Co Ltd.

ISBN 9780224089845

"I ... remember ... being walked to a
post in the ... middle of nowhere
and told to count to 500

1 2 3 4 5 6 7 8 9 . . . . .

I'M SLOWLY getting used
to the idea

chapter 2.

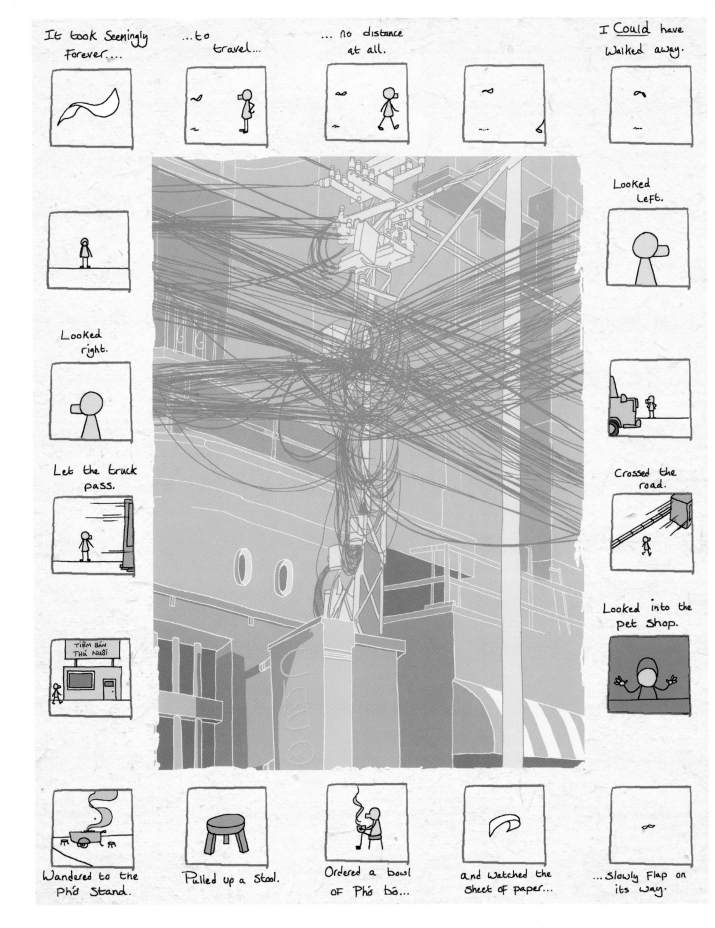

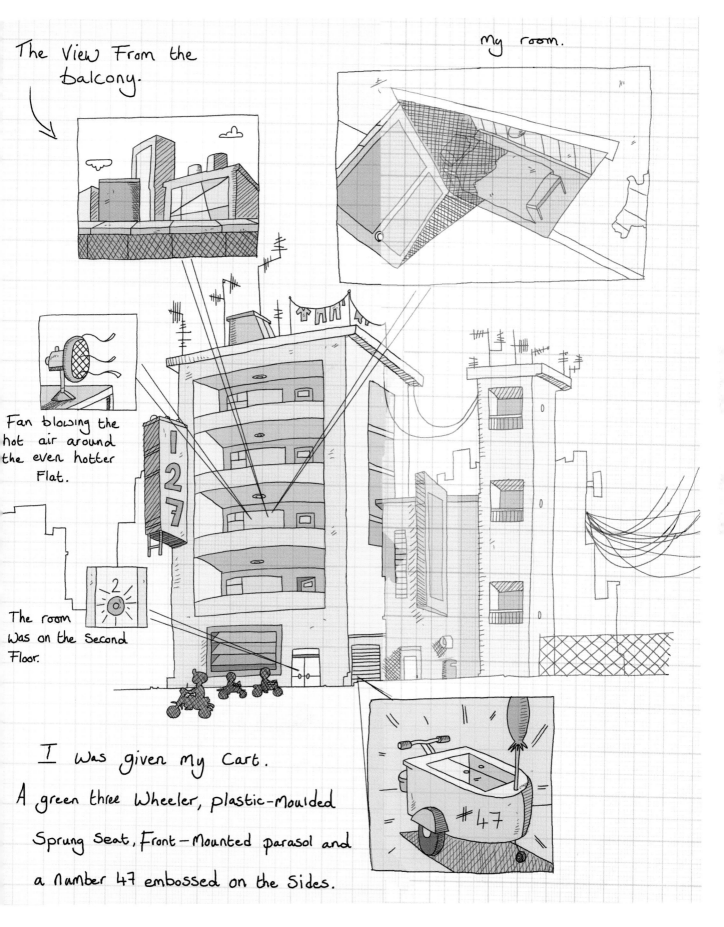

The View From the balcony.

my room.

Fan blowing the hot air around the even hotter Flat.

The room Was on the Second Floor.

I Was given my Cart.
A green three Wheeler, plastic-moulded
Sprung Seat, Front-Mounted parasol and
a Number 47 embossed on the Sides.

#47

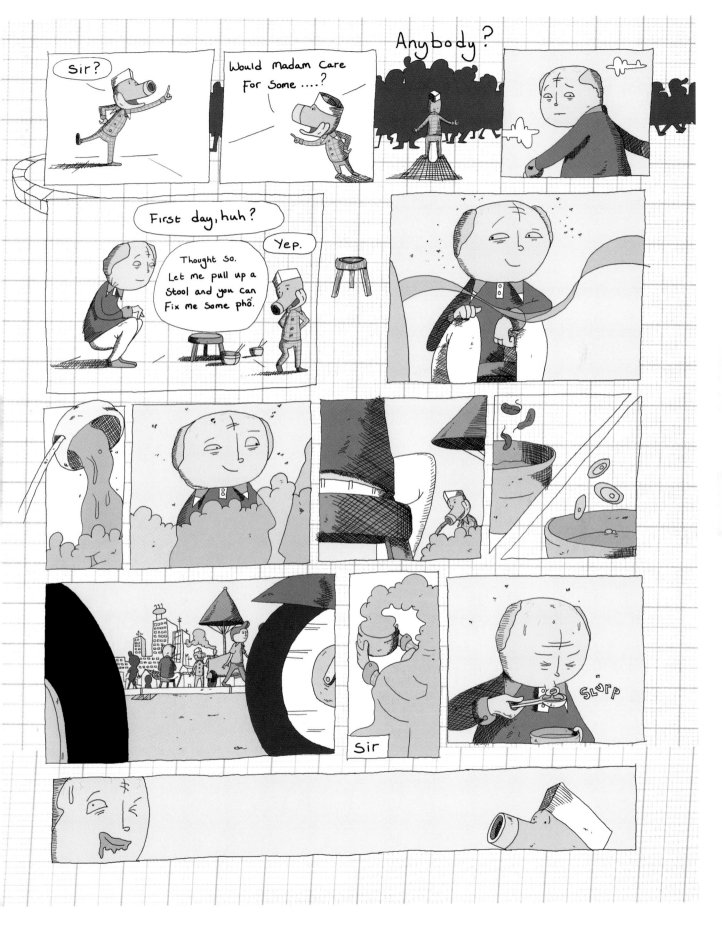

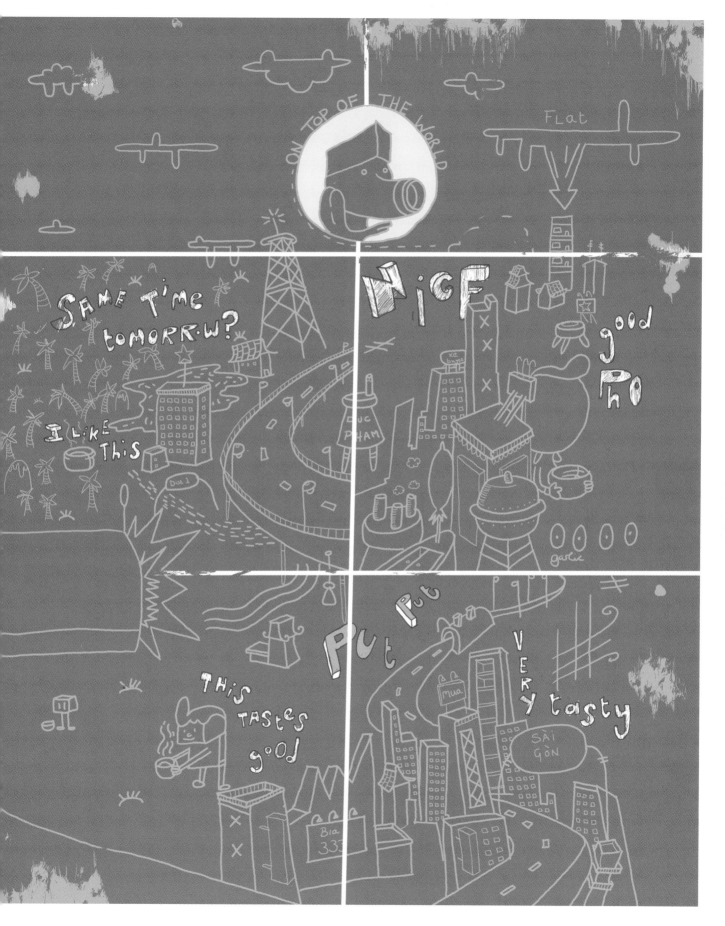

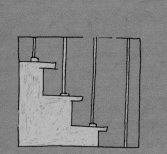   

Chapter 3

127 Công Quỳnh
Dist 1.

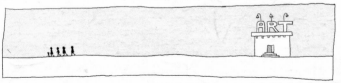

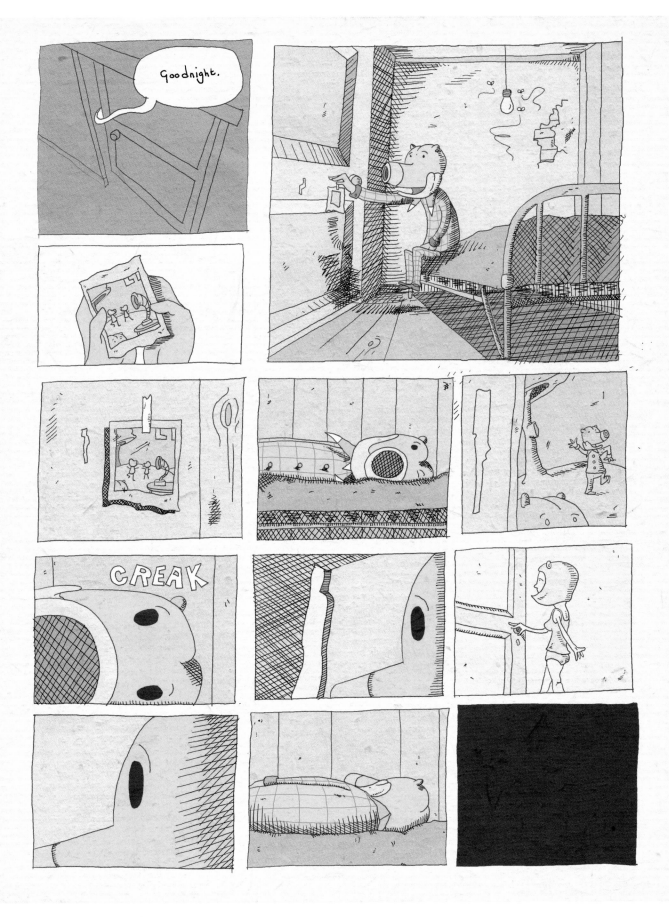

Every morning I step into the street and the warm air envelops me. I join the city streets overloaded with mopeds and bicycles. From these bustling masses I have found a band of true and loyal friends.

The old man is always my first customer of the day. I take my breakfast with him and when we sit on the stools and talk about the morning's issues, the city fades into the background.

the pretty shy lady

those just passing through

the dreamers

lots of dreamers.

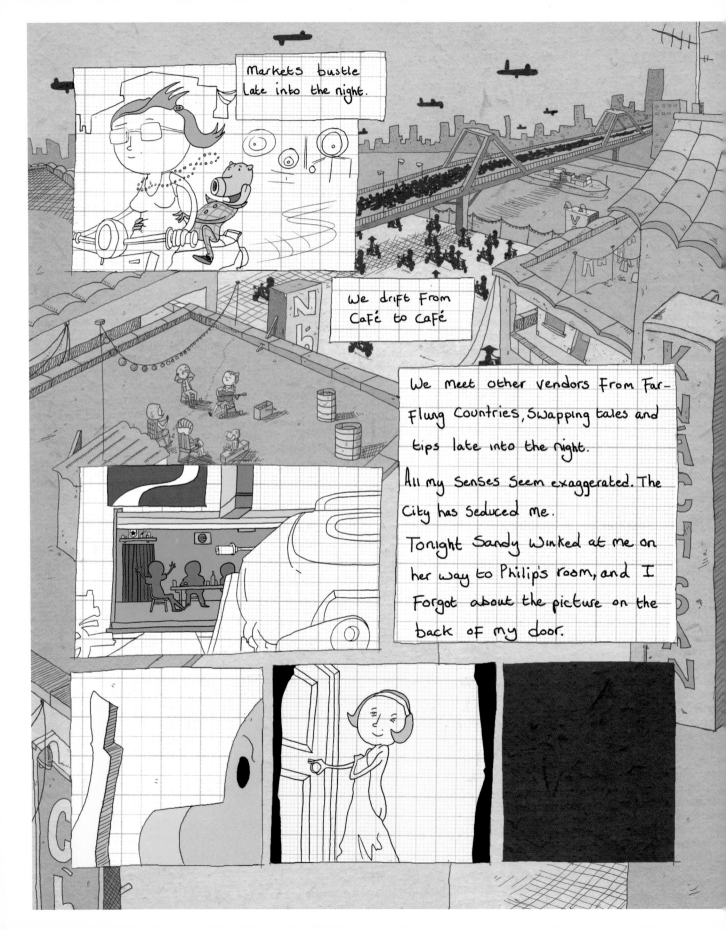

The days that change your life start like any other day.

And in a moment you are sent on a course

that would have seemed impossible a second ago.

Electric winch to take heavy rucksacks
up the stairwell.

Hi Phil.

G'day, Little Blue. Sandy's already upstairs. Have to say she's acting a bit odd.

Chicks, eh?

Er, Yeah, chicks.

Rummage

Jingle

Squeak

Hello...? Sandy?

FUD

FUD

Hi

I just love watching the city going about its business.

Not really.

Are all cities like this?

Well I'm from a small village in England, that like most of the UK it is grey and a bit tepid. So firstly I guess I need to feel the heat in my bones, the kinda heat you feel in your lungs. I also like the sound of flip flops. Shallow Huh!

Swirl

Not really

What else? I think better when I'm moving "You can't hit a moving target", right? I also like to have everything in one bag, cutting back to the essentials - couple of changes of clothes, camera, of course, the various chargers and a notebook. You're not the only one, L.B. I've seen you scribbling..... Am I in your book?

crumple

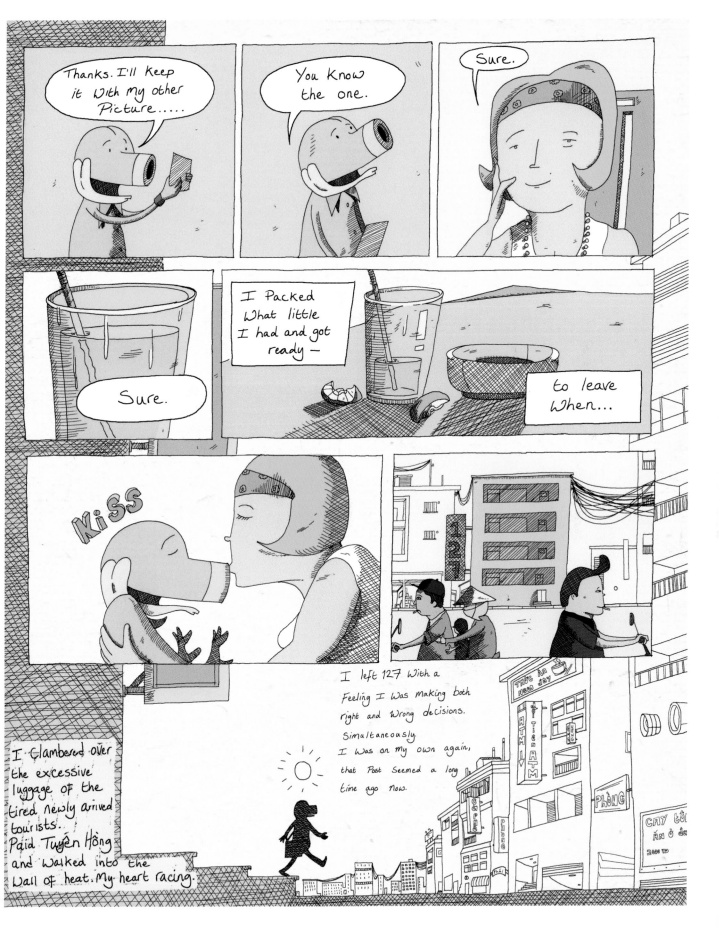

Chapter 5.

Sink Like
SAKA PAINT
12 KHÁCH SẠN 12
PHỞ BÒ
MÁY LẤY TIỀN.
PHO BO.
TRÁI CÂY
GẠO
Polished Stones.

Will write tomorrow too busy Eating and

look at → Learning!!

Fried Fish, tôm xāo tǒi - Sticky Shrimp with garlic.

→ CA chiên Banh BAO Chiên - Donuts

TÔM RANG me → shrimp with tamarind.

nghieu HẤP XẢ → Steamed-clams with lemongrass.

Cháo

Canh chay

① Place the round rice paper in a warm bowl of water, until soft.

② lay on a damp tea cloth.

③ In the middle add lettuce, cucumber, spring onion and carrot.

④ Add the prawns, mint, rice stick noodles (cooked, drained, cooled), coriander.

⑤

Roll the outer edges in, followed by the bottom. And continue to gently roll from the bottom.

⑥

⑦

When half way through rolling, you can use the stalk of a chopped spring onion as a "stick" by placing it in the centre of the roll.

⑧

Chilli Sauce

chilli Paste 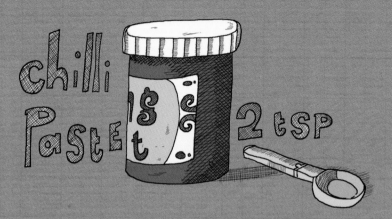 2 tsp

 1/4 cup water

Hoi Sin Sauce  1/2 cup

 1 shallot

 1 tsp Rice Vinegar

 2 tsp Chopped Peanuts

Hoisin dipping Sauce

EATEN in Phan Tiêt

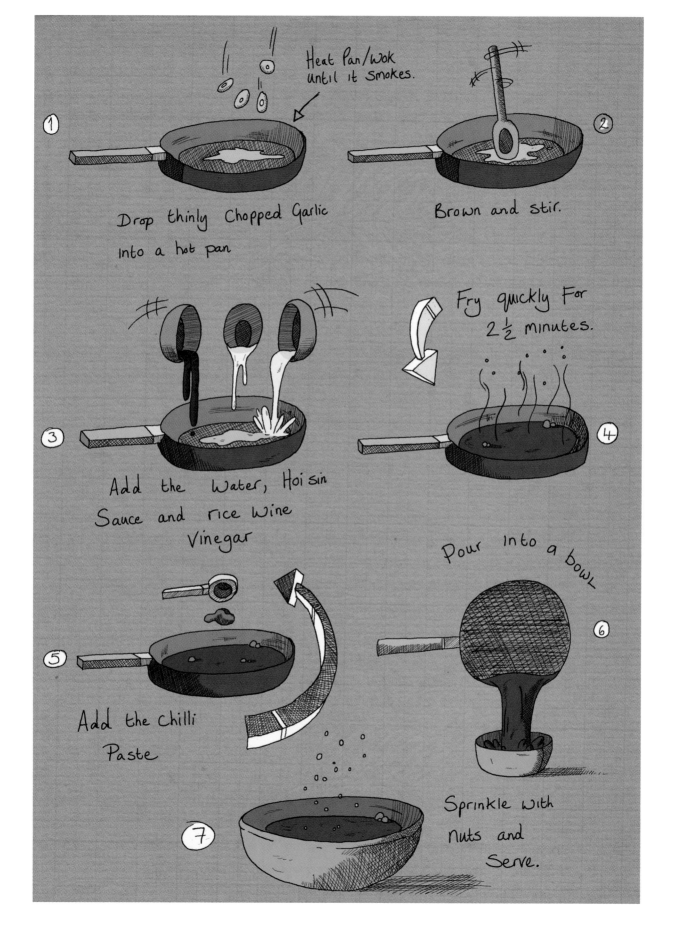

KHỔ QUA

(Bitter Melon)

Hollow out Melon then stuff with pork. Then Simmer in a light chicken or pork broth. Garnish with Coriander.

RAU MUỐNG
(Water Spinach)

Not a relative of Western Spinach. Prized due to the Contrast between the Crunchy stems and mild-tasting leaves. Good for Stir Fries.

XÌ DÂU
(Soy Sauce)

Different from the Chinese Soy Sauce. It is lighter in Colour and different in taste and Saltiness. It Won't Stain Food black.

BÁNH PHỞ
(Rice Sticks)

Made from rice flour. 3 Sizes — Wide, used in Stir Fries, The medium is used in phở (it is the most popular), the Thin is More Suitable in noodle Soups.

NGO
(Coriander)

A Must in Vietnamese Cooking. Refrigerate wrapped in a Moist paper towel in a plastic bag.

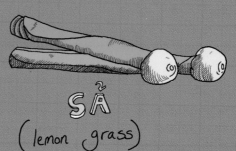

SẢ
(lemon grass)

Cut the bulb portion up to the place where the leaves begin to branch. Peel off tough outer leaves, Crush slightly the White underlayer before using.
IF you can only get dried lemon grass, Soak in Warm Water for 1 hour before use.

CỦ KIỆU NGÂM GIÂM ĐUỜNG
(Pickled Shallots)

Young tender bulbs packed in Vinegar, Sugar and Salt, used as a condiment to grilled Foods and Noodle dishes.

MÌ TRỨNG

Two Varieties, the long thin Cantonese Style called 'don Mein' used in deep Frying. The Fatter noodles called 'Fu don Mein' are used in Soups. Fresh noodles are preferred.

← egg noodles

CÀ TÍM
(Aubergine)

This thin, seedless Variety has a sweet flavour with no hint of bitterness. Unlike the Western Aubergine it does not require Peeling, Salting or rinsing.

MĂNG
(bamboo Shoots)

Two types: Winter and Spring. Winter shoots are best, they are dug up before they grow too big so are tender. Spring shoots are larger and more stringy.

ỚT
(Chillies)

Two types: 1st the large red or green Variety are mild and used for garnish, Sometimes Whole.
The Second are thin and Much hotter. They are used for Seasoning - usually Sold in mixed bags.

NUOG COT DUA
(Coconut milk)

The clear liquid is used in Soft drinks or as a tenderizing agent.
The White 'Meat' is grated and provides the milk. Do not Confuse Coconut milk with Coconut Cream. The latter is a heavily Sweetened Coconut product.

TÔM KHÔ
(Dried Shrimp)

Shelled, dried and Salted. They have a pungent flavour and are used in Small quantities to flavour dishes. The larger and darker the Shrimp the better the quality. Soak for 30 mins before use. Keep the Soaking liquid to give a lift to Soups.

tốt nhất

Canh Bí Rọ Nam Đức
(Braised Pumpkin in Coconut Milk)

- 2 CUPS Pumpkin, 2 Cups Coconut Milk
- 2 tableSpoons Polygonum leaves, ½ Cup Mushrooms, ½ cup Courgette, Salt, 2 Cups Sweet Potato, ½ cup Coconut Cream, ½ Cup Peanuts, 1 tbsp Sugar.

- Pumpkin and Coconut Milk in **DEEP Pan** — boil — Cook Until Pumpkin ½ done. Add Spuds and Mushrooms — Reduce heat and **SIMMER**. Add Cream + Peanuts + Courgette and bring back to boil. Season with Salt + Sugar.

Xghêu Xào ớt (Spicy Clams)

36 Razor Clams, 1tsp Veg oil, 2 tsp Fish Sauce, 3 oz Ginger, 1 tsp garlic Sauce, 2 Spring Onions, 1 bunch Corriander, 2 Cloves of Garlic

Put clams in bowl of Water to Cover — in Fridge 30 Min — drain — repeat **TWICE** More.

Heat Wok on high heat, add garlic, Ginger - Stir - add clams, Chilli Sauce - Scatter Onion/Corriander on top. Cover and Cook till Clams Open.

Mục Ch
2 ts

Bánh Tôm

1 lb raw Prawn, 1 Cup Flour, 1 Cup Water, Salt, Veg oil, Pepper, 1 Spud

Peeled - Cut thin then Cut into Shoe Strings

Wash Prawns — Jay, Mash ½ Prawn — Cut remaining in half length Ways. Put Flour in bowl. Add Water gently. Add Salt and Pepper.

Add Prawn Paste to batter, add Spuds Place tomato Prawns in the batter - Put in taste - drop in oil — Ham — Fry until golden - Serve with lettuce ✦ Nước Chấm

---

Nước Chấm

4 red chillies, 2 cloves garlic 1 tsp Sugar, 2 limes (Peeled Chopped) 1 tsp Water, 1 tsp Vinegar. 5 tsp Nước Mắm — Fish Sauce

- Pound garlic — Add chillies — Paste
- Add Sugar ✦ lime — Pound to Pulp.
- Put in small bowl, add Water, Vinegar and Fish Sauce

Add Nuts, Fried garlic, Spicy Onions, Sweet basil, Mint

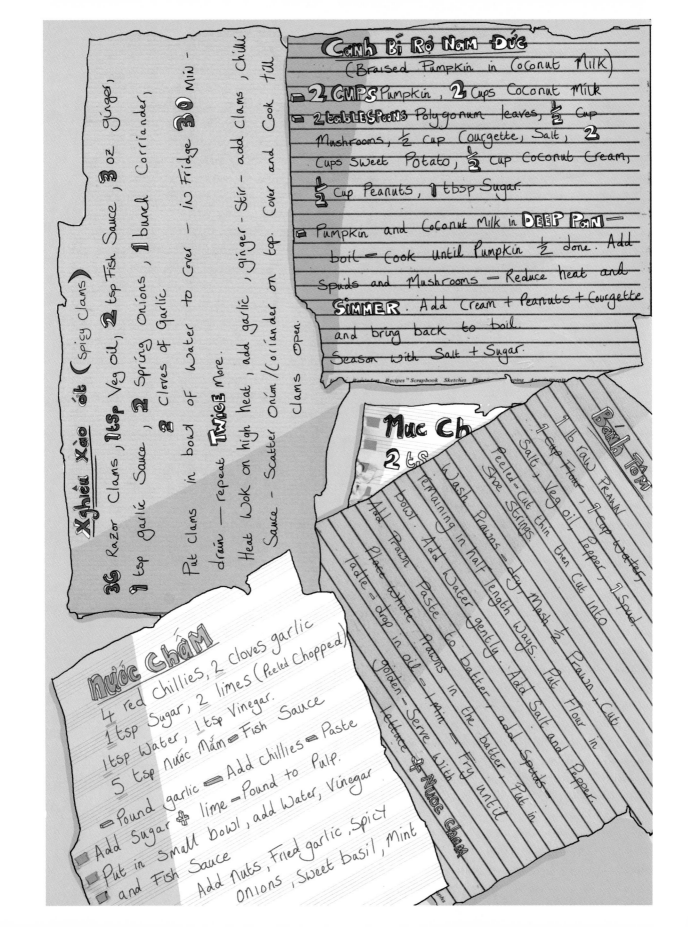

It's your Food that everyone has come here For, Little Blue. When they Come to Saigon, being business people, they eat in the Swanky hotels all on the Company account. And they Miss out on the real Food— Street Food.

..IN.

The Kitchen gleamed as the Cool UV light Fizzed into liFe My Pho Stand Seemed as antiquated as it Was distant.

Click

And that's Where You Come....

= Fizz =

As I Spoke about What I intended to do I got the Feeling She Wasn't really listening Although She looked at Me intently.

"BLink"

Just one thing.

"PLINK"

Rummage

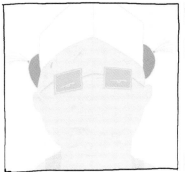

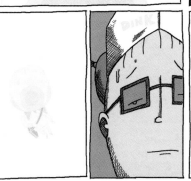

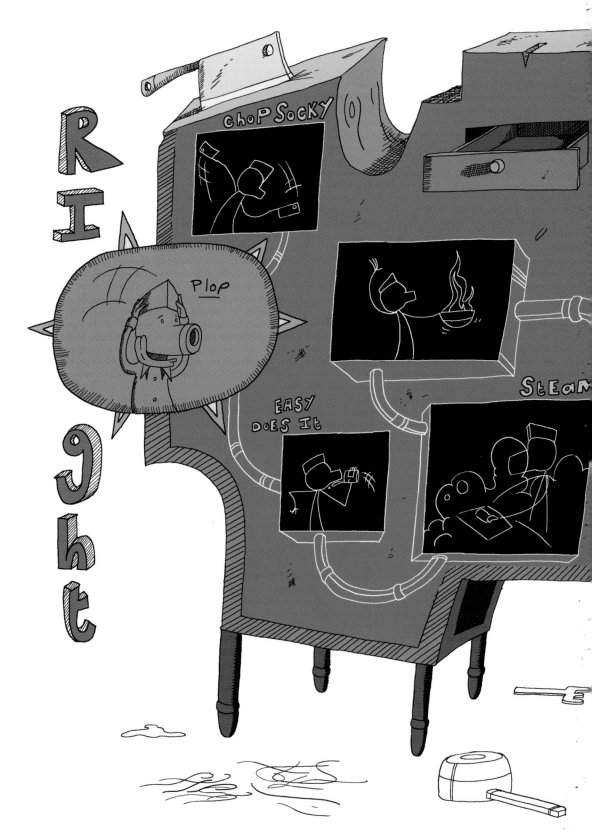

TÔM TẨM BỘT CHIÊN GIÒN

Adding beer to the batter lightens it and the hint of 'bitterness' it brings adds depth to the dish.

Serve with Chilli Sauce

Bánh ít Lá Ga is sticky rice with coconut and green bean wrapped in a banana leaf. **Bánh ít thôm thit** is with a meat and shrimp filling

Pot for steaming leaves.

Banana leaves are put in hot water to soften them

chanh Đá

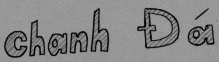

A simple drink of ice, squeezed lemon juice and a table-spoon of sugar. Works well after food.

Cháo

A hearty rice porridge containing prawns, fish balls and long beans (Dua Dua) for their crunch.

Cá Hấp gừng

The fish is steamed whole and then placed on a plate, with the host using chopsticks, will put portions of fish into each guest's bowl.

OtHER good THingS

Bò Tùng Xèo

Hot Clay Pot With Warm Coals.

Beef Marinated in Soy Sauce, ginger, chilli, Salt and Pepper.

Sits on your table

KHÔ MỰC

Bought From bicycles. The dried Squid is Shredded and gently Fried Then Served With a Sour powder Wrapped in newspaper.

Nước Mía

The Sugar Cane is pulped and the Juice Squeezed out. Then it is Poured over chipped ice. Ask For a Squeeze of lime with it.

Comes in a Plastic bag So it Can be hung on the handlebars of a Moped or bike.

BÁNH XÈO

Banana Filling either Caramelised or Fresh.

Swirl the batter outwards From the middle of a hot Wok.

Bia Tươi Hơi

Bought in Street bars and drunk Sitting on small plastic Stools on the pavement. Cheaper than bottled beers as it is decanted From a large drum into 1-litre plastic bottles.

GÀ KHO

A northern Chicken dish. In Saigon and the Mekong the Chicken is usually Sautéed With chilli and garlic First.

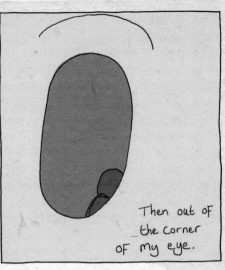

Then out of the corner of my eye.

A Face that looked so Familiar.

HOW TO DRINK cà Phê

2. Pour a little boiling water in. Wait 10 seconds. Then fill up the Filter.

1. Remove Screen. Add 3 heaped teaspoons of coffee. Put Screen firmly onto coffee.

3. Let coffee drip onto ice in glass.

4. Enjoy.

So Familiar.

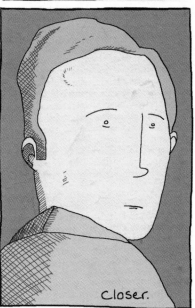

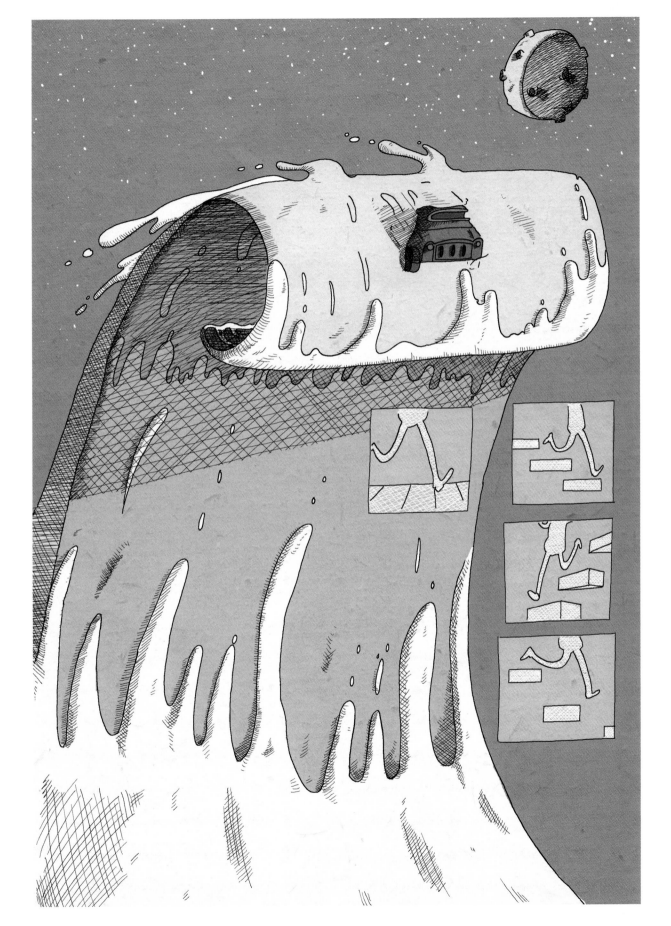

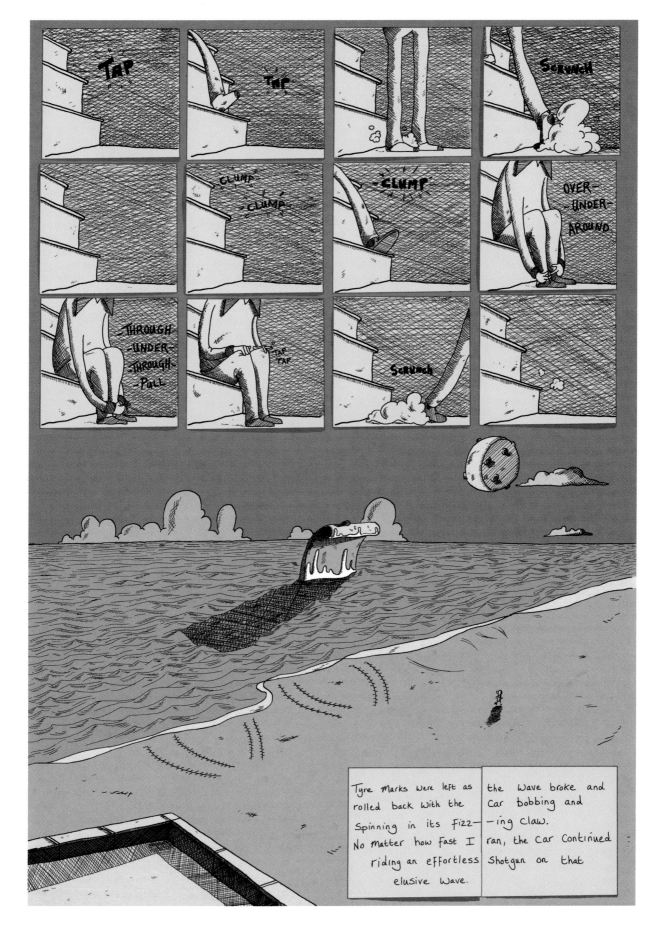

Tyre marks were left as rolled back with the Spinning in its Fizz— No matter how fast I riding an effortless elusive Wave.

the wave broke and car bobbing and —ing claw. ran, the car continued Shotgun on that

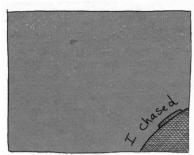
I chased

the   Wave   all

night

HỒNG DI

Bungalows For Rent.

Past deserted Motels.

Until

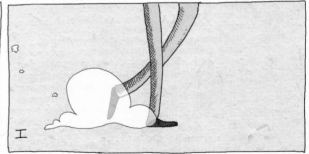
I

could

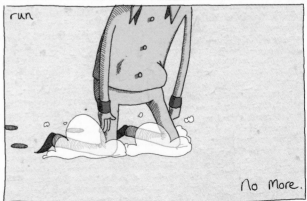
run

No More.

The Fair was as vivid and surreal as my dream, only slightly more sickly sweet in smell.

'It was, however, warmer and drier than where I had been only two hours ago.

I walked confidently on the terra firma, strangely righteous.'

HA HA HAHAHAHA HAHAT

As I pushed through the crowd I could smell the different conditioner on each person's clothes. My senses were alive.

I believe they call moments like these pivotal.
I felt a twinge of neuralgia in my temples, my breaths became shallow my head swam—almost as though I was drowning again.

is this it?

From a piece of paper wrapped around my face to it being taped to the back of my door, to here.
All the time I had felt special but now I wanted to shrink like a salted snail back into the crowd.
Everything I hoped for, everything that piece of fluttering paper had offered, suddenly came crashing to nothing.

Nothing but a poorly constructed stage that, creaked and threatened to, collapse with each movement.
To add insult to injury they were performing in the car park.

I don't know who was more shocked.

He was bigger than me, could he be a cousin of mine, or even a brother?

Just like it had
happened before, a
skrunch of tyres and
a cloud of dust.

And again it
was gone.

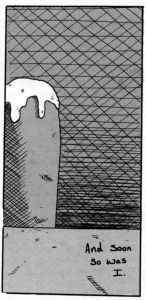

And soon
so was
I.

Mui
NE
3o Km

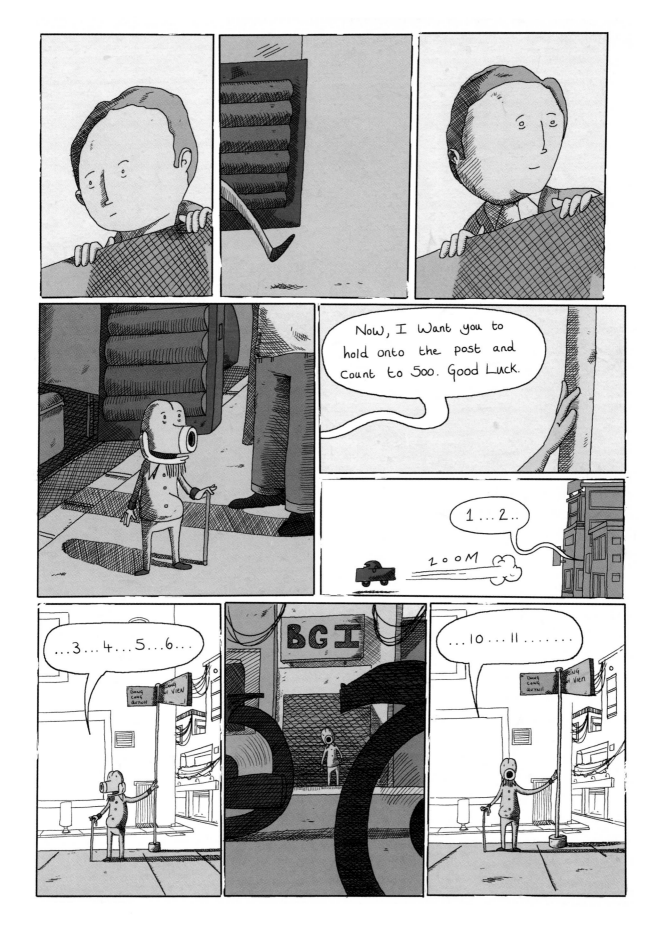

Hello.

I'm Joe.

I'm Little Blue.

I Know.

Come.

DONG CONG QUYNH

DONG Bui Vien

It's so quiet here. You'd never know we were in a city.

Yeah...

...So Joe.

I have to ask. How do you know my name?

The man in the car told me. The same man who brought you here. Is this making sense?

errr.

He was surprised to see you at the party in Mui Ne

You see, he brings us here to give us another chance.

To start again and shed your past. I'm afraid this is my last chance.

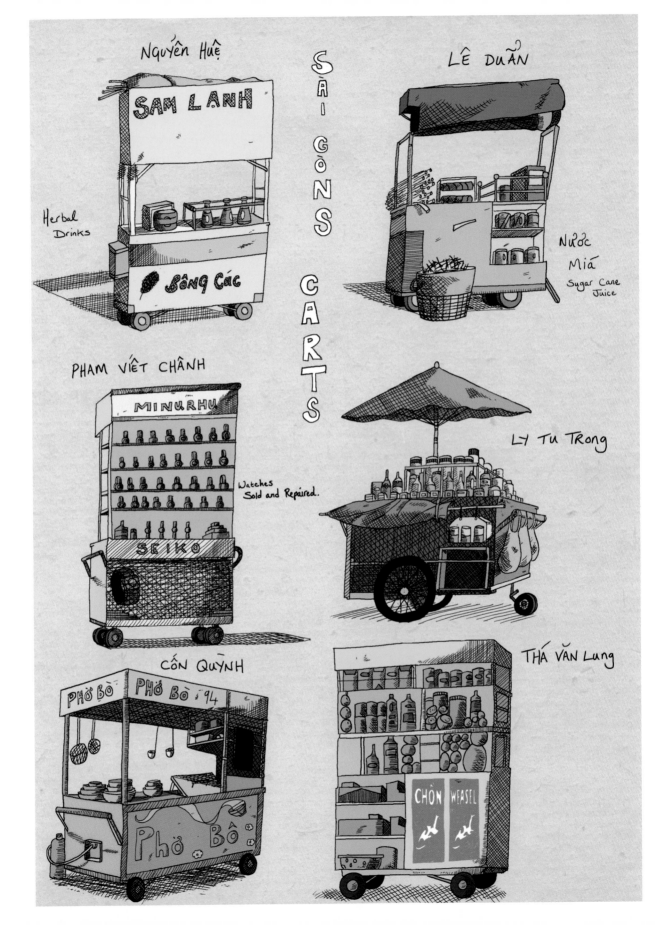

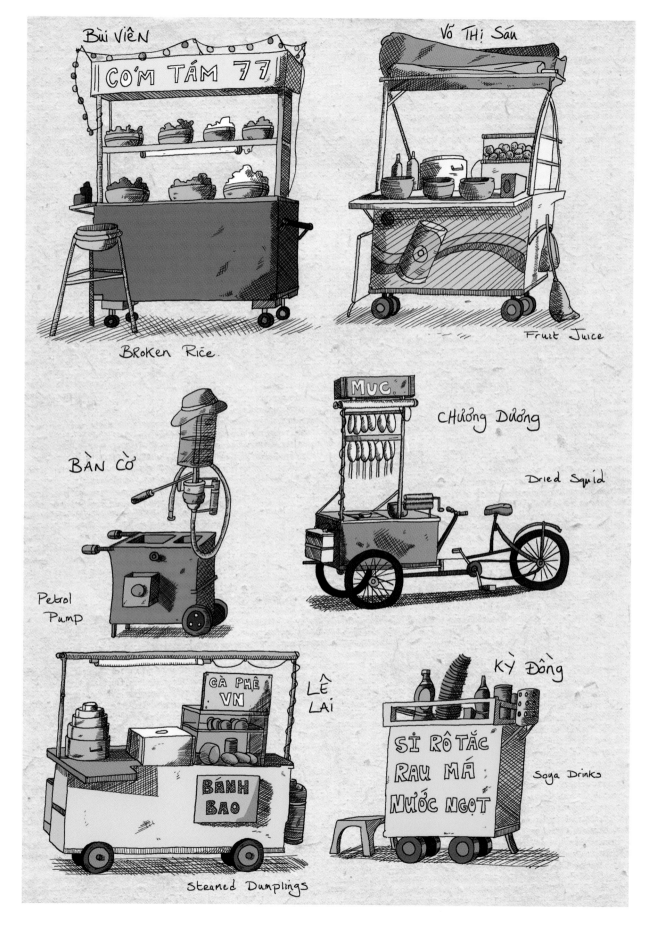

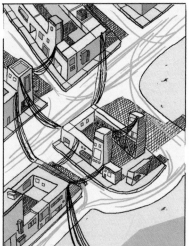
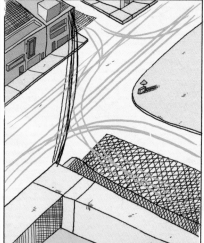

The old man looked
surprised.

SSSSsshhhhh

Very
surprised

It had been a long journey to get to this moment.

You're not .....

...Sandy.

Yeah, that's right. I'm Kim.

No worries though. I get that a lot, it's the hair, right?

She gave me the dye before she left. How do you know her?

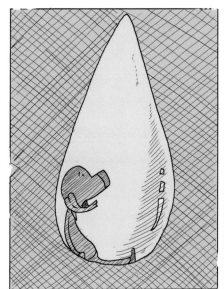
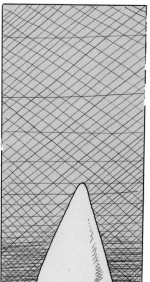
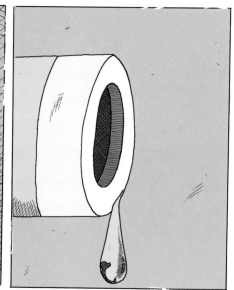

With each bowl I felt a growing connection with the city

I ate 3 bowls of phở bò and then did the only thing I could think of — absolutely nothing.

Everyone looked different. But oddly still the same.

Young. Hopeful.

Moving Forward. Moving on.

My logic was, for what it's worth, wherever Sandy happened to be,

She could, should she want to, find me here. On our corner.

The one constant in this city.

Little Blue's
Phố Bò

For the Broth

2 onions

6 lb of bones — Knuckle (beef)

Water — **5** litres

Spices in Cheese Cloth bag:
Roast the Spices for 10 mins

1 tbsp Coriander Seeds

6 Star anise

1 tbsp Fennel

2 cloves garlic

2 Sticks Cinnamon

1 Cardamon Pod.

Pinch of Salt

dash of Fish Sauce

Hard boil the bones for 15 min's then drain, rinse bones, refill.

Roast onions and garlic.

Put above ↑ + Spice bag back in and boil for 3 hrs (Keep removing build up on surface).

In a bowl place a handful of Rice noodle, thinly sliced Flank Steak – and then... ludle in boiling broth (it will cook noodles + steak)

hành giấm (sliced white onion in vinegar) another side dish which cuts the fattiness of the beef

then →

For People To Garnish With

Next to the bowl place dishes of bean sprouts, thai basil, lime wedges and chillies

thai Basil

Bean Sprouts

Lime Wedges / sliced chilli

The two of them brought implements for me to cook my phở with.

I survived on one bowl a day, usually eaten around 11 am. In the heat I tended to sweat all the liquids out.

Afterwards we would chat and eventually they would leave to continue with their own lives.

The locals at first found me an oddity

But soon they passed by as though I wasn't there.

The skyline crept up into the endless warm skies. With each day my view differed.

One day there was just one.

I didn't ask whether it was his patience that had run its course or if nature had.

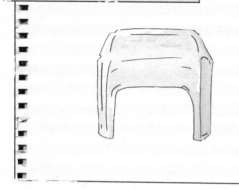

And on a Sunday quite soon after that...

...it was just me.

I waited till the following Thursday.

I felt a pattern emerging: rest followed by movement, followed by tiredness and then the inevitable desire for motion. I was beginning to grasp it.

EVERYONE GOES
AWAY IN THE
END.